© 2006 by Faber Music Ltd
First published by Faber Music Ltd in 2006
3 Queen Square, London WC1N 3AU

Compiled by Lucy Holliday
Arranged by Alex Davis & Tom Fleming
Edited by Lucy Holliday

Designed by Lydia Merrills-Ashcroft

Printed in England by Caligraving Ltd
All rights reserved

ISBN10: 0-571-52696-9
EAN13: 978-0-571-52696-3

To buy Faber Music publications or to find out about the full range of titles available,
please contact your local music retailer or Faber Music sales enquiries:

Faber Music Ltd, Burnt Mill, Elizabeth Way, Harlow, CM20 2HX England
Tel: +44(0)1279 82 89 82 Fax: +44(0)1279 82 89 83
sales@fabermusic.com fabermusic.com

Albion

Words and Music by Peter Doherty

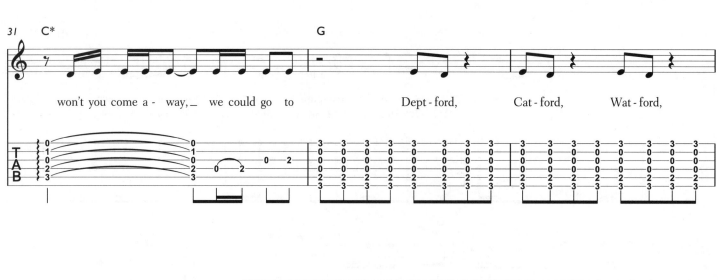

won't you come a - way,__ we could go to Dept - ford, Cat - ford, Wat - ford,

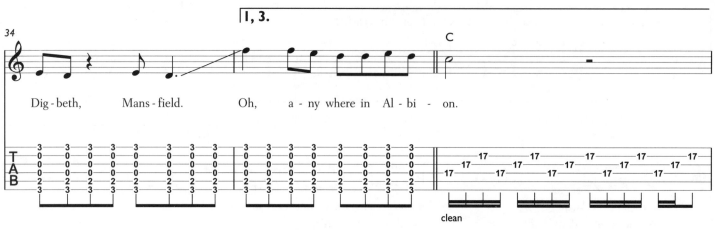

Dig - beth, Mans - field. Oh, a - ny where in Al - bi - on.

clean

A - ny - where in Al - bi - on.__

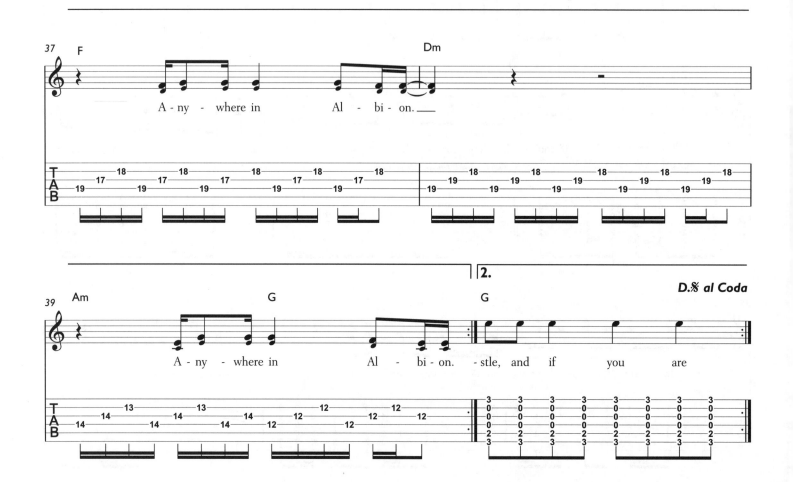

A - ny - where in Al - bi - on. -stle, and if you are

Chorus 2:
If you're looking for a cheap sort all glint with perspiration
There's a four mile queue outside the disused power station
Now come away, oh say you'll come away, go to
Satsworth, Senworth, Weovil, Woomoyle, Newcastle

Chorus 3:
And if you are looking for a cheap tart, don't glint with perspiration
There's a five mile queue outside the disused power station
Now come away, won't you come away, we'll go to
Bedtown, Oldham, Nunthorpe, Rowlan, Bristol
Anywhere in Albion.

Bullets

Words and Music by Thomas Smith, Christopher Urbanowicz,
Russell Leetch and Edward Lay

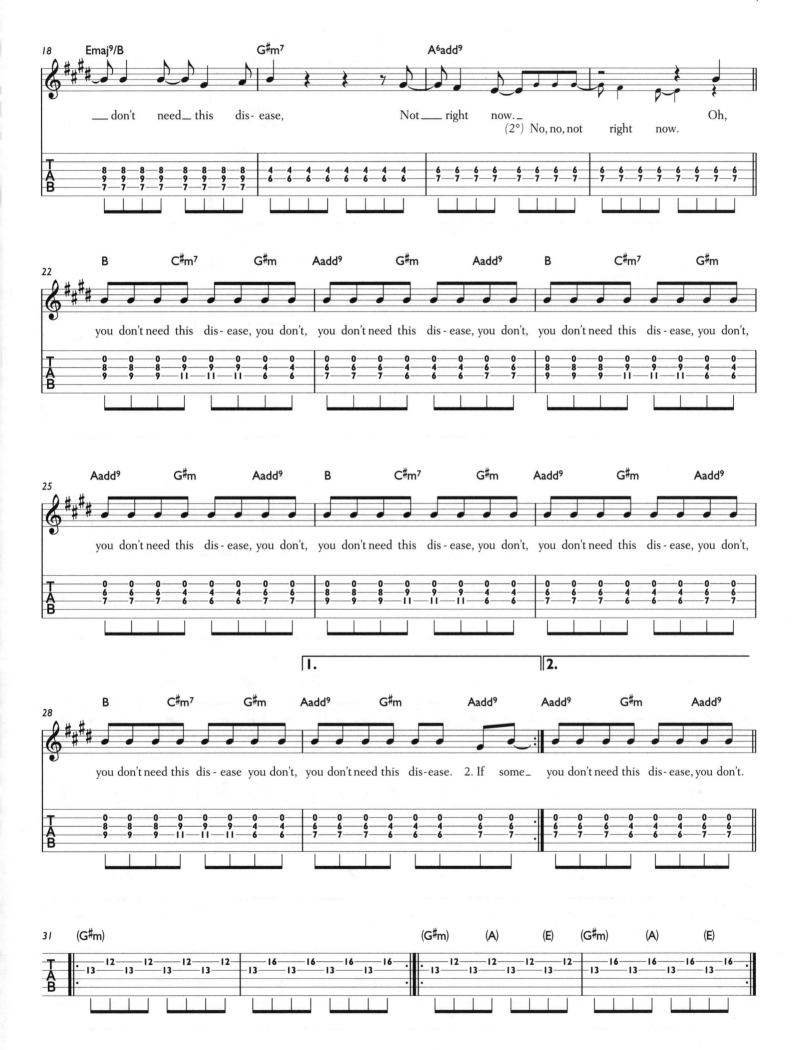

8

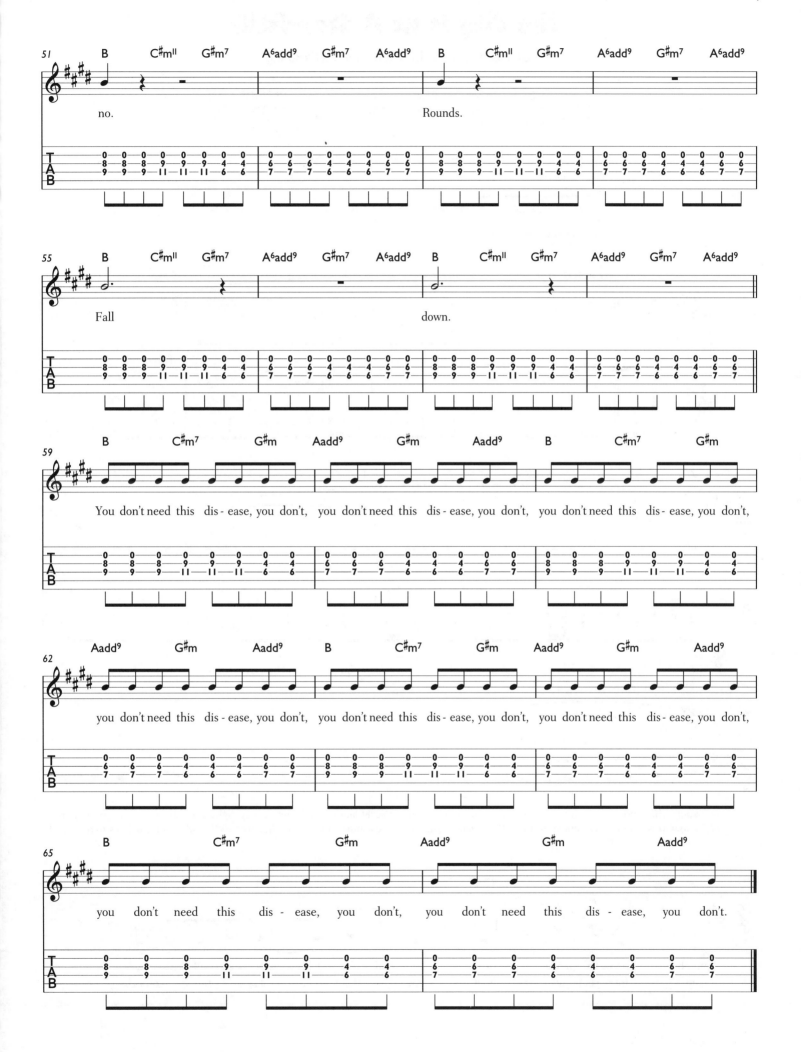

The City Is At A Standstill

Words and Music by Liam Thomas Pickering

(1.) know this world is vi-cious dar-ling, let's make tracks now. We'll black out all the ci-ty lights and drink 'til we both grow
(2.) know this world is vi-cious dar-ling, let's make tracks now. We'll burn up ev-'ry his-tory book and start our lives here. Drink

numb, then lay down to sleep. I feel like I ran all day.
up, for-get all a-bout the loss that a life-time brought our

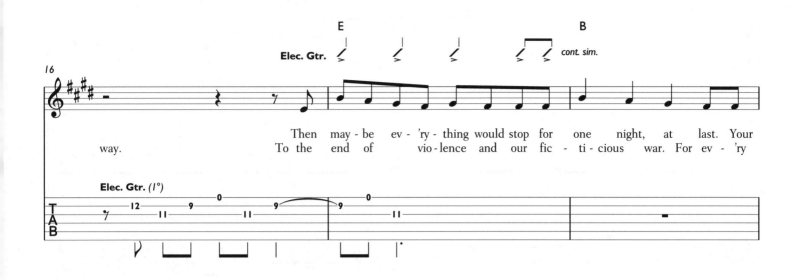

Then may-be ev-'ry-thing would stop for one night, at last. Your
To the end of vio-lence and our fic-ti-cious war. For ev-'ry

way.

eyes are look-ing bright girl, like fire-flies caught in a glass. You scrub up pret-ty well,
crook-ed po-li-ti-cian there's a thou-sand more. Drink up, for-get all___ a-

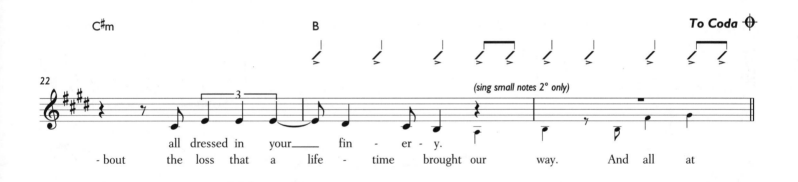

(sing small notes 2° only)

To Coda

all dressed in your___ fin-er-y. And all at
- bout the loss that a life - time brought our way.

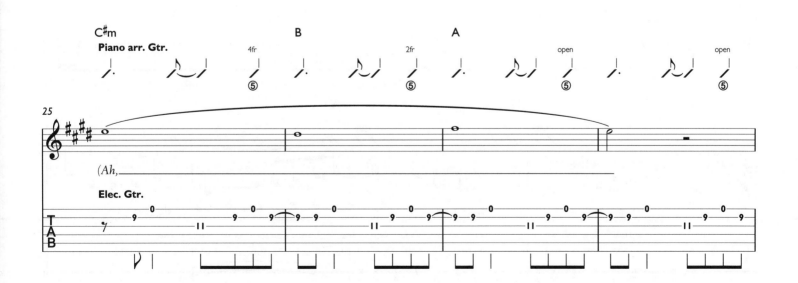

(Ah,___

Elec. Gtr.

Dolls (Sweet Rock & Roll)

Words and Music by Bobby Gillespie, Andrew Innes, Gary Mounfield and Martin Duffy

Elec. Gtr. I plays Fig. I

Forever Lost

Words and Music by Romeo Stodart

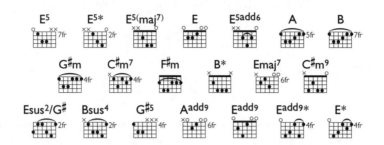

 = 150

Electric Guitar

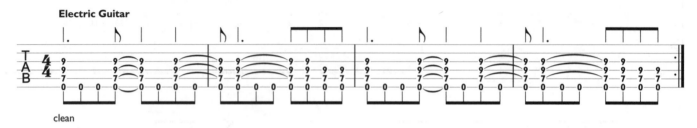

clean

distortion

1. Dar - ling,___ what you gon - na do now,___ now that you no -
2. Dar - ling,___ what you gon - na say now,___ now that you no -

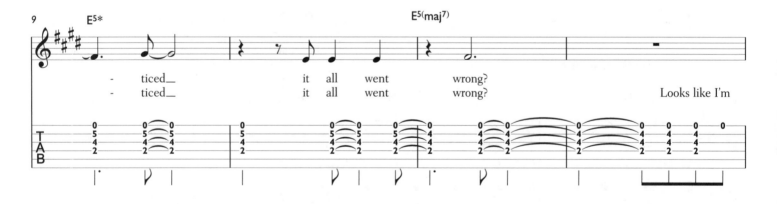

- ticed___ it all went wrong?
- ticed___ it all went wrong?   Looks like I'm

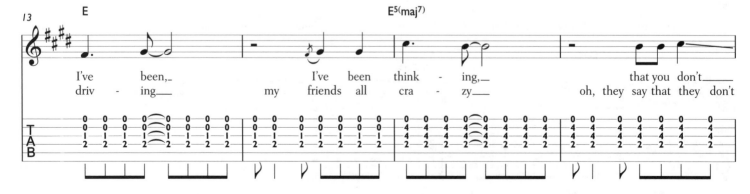

I've been,___ I've been think - ing,___ that you don't___
driv - ing___ my friends all cra - zy___ oh, they say that they don't

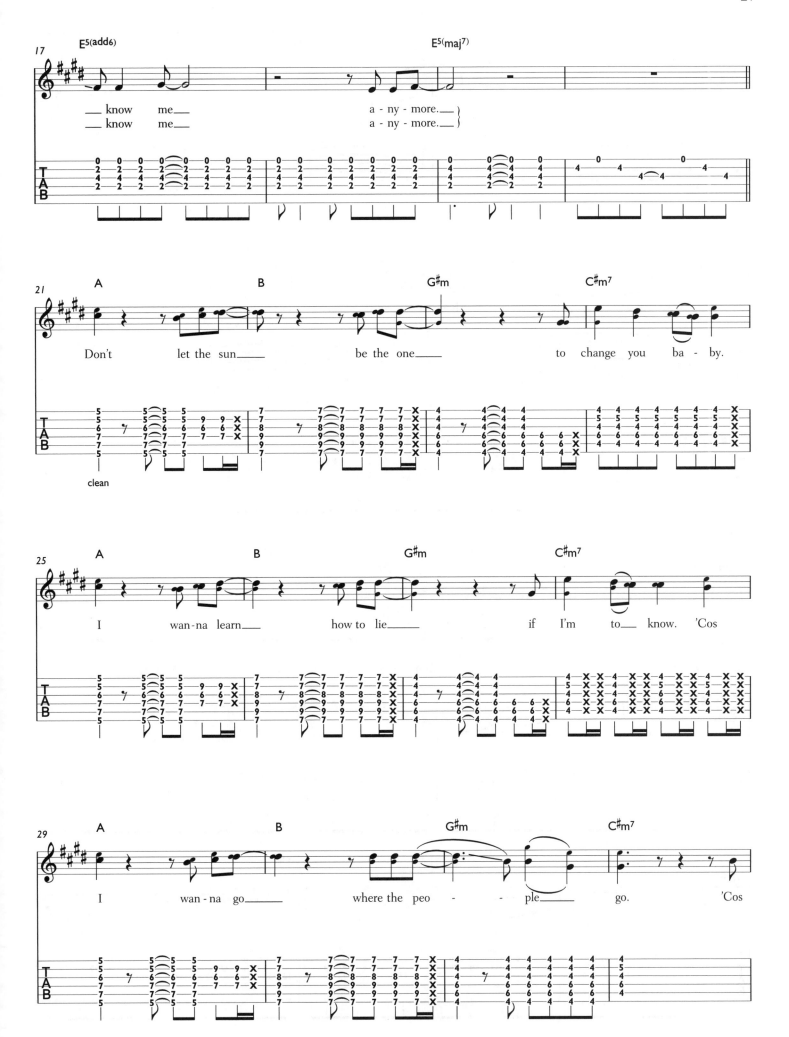

Heart In A Cage

Words and Music by Julian Casablancas

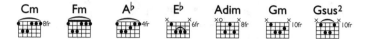

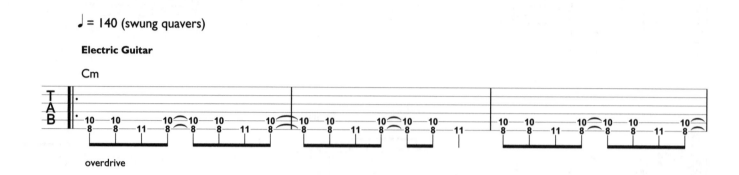

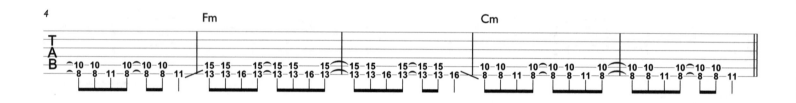

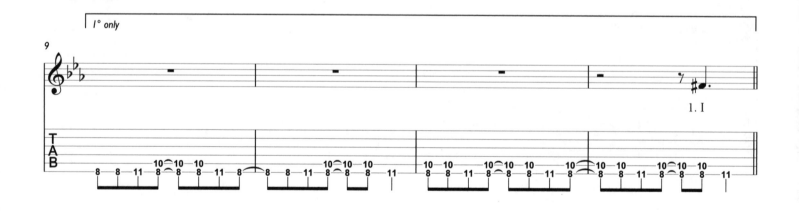

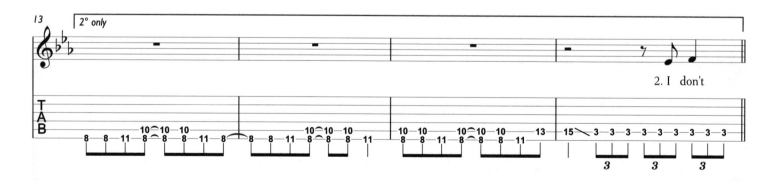

Keep Us Together

Words and Music by James Walsh, James Stelfox,
Barry Westhead and Benjamin Byrne

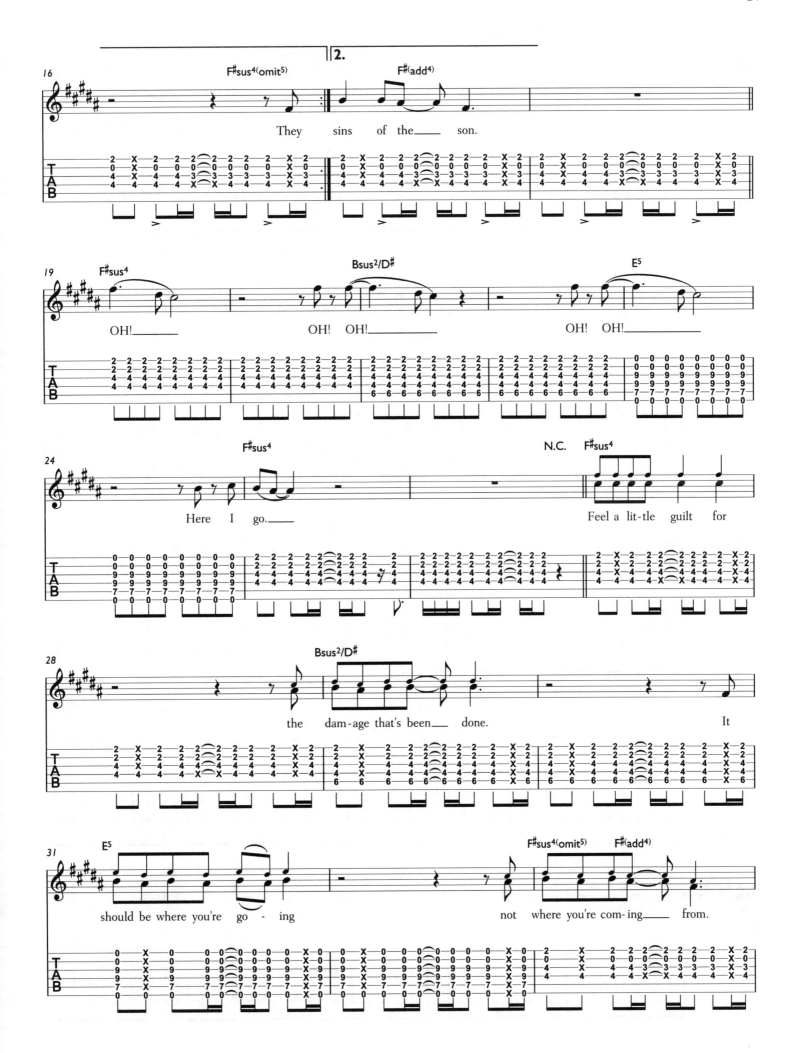

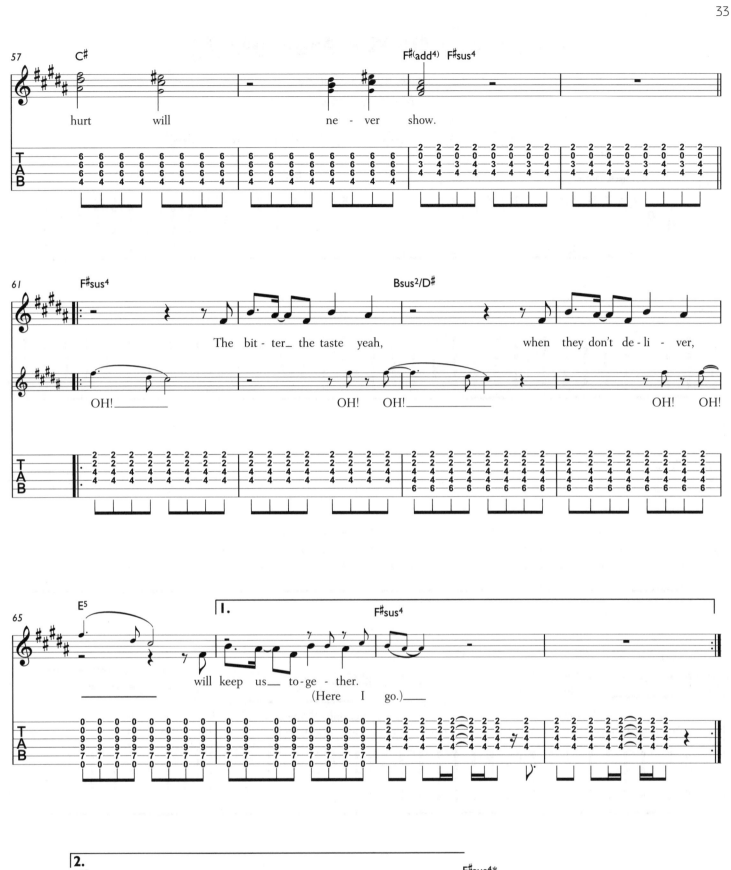

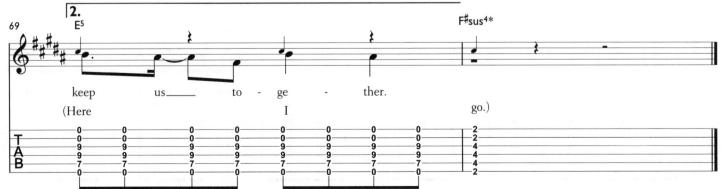

Leaders Of The Free World

Words by Guy Garvey
Music by Elbow

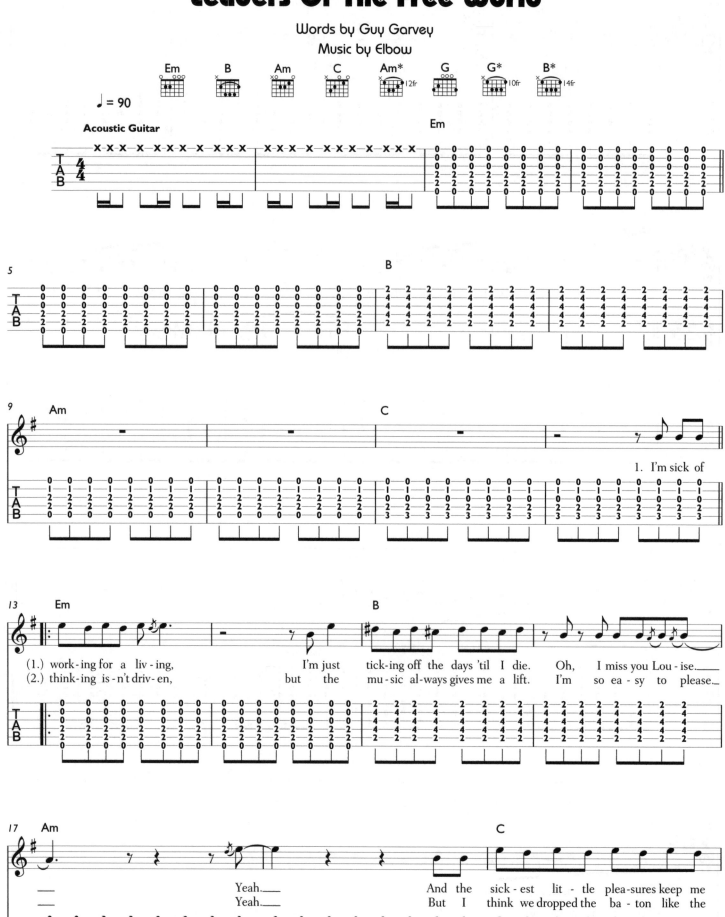

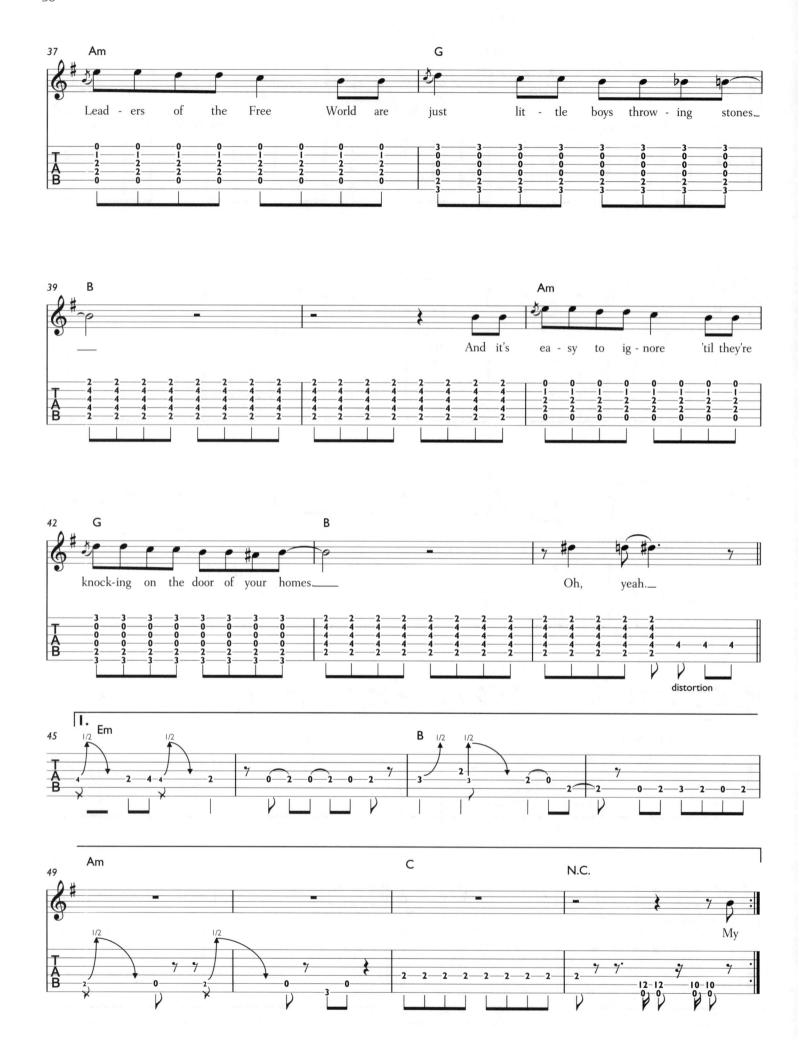

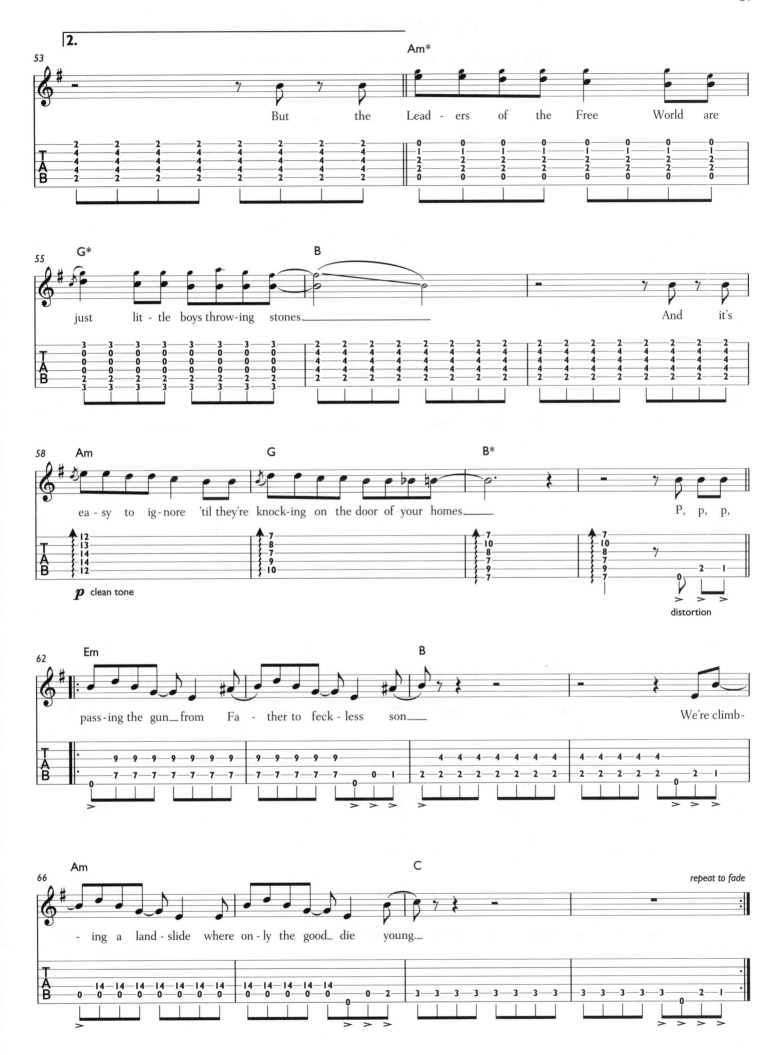

Like Eating Glass

Words and Music by Kele Okereke, Russell Lissack,
Gordon Moakes and Matt Tong

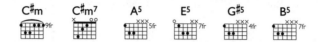

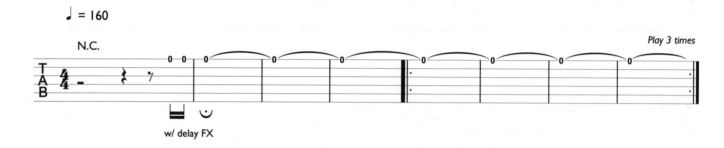

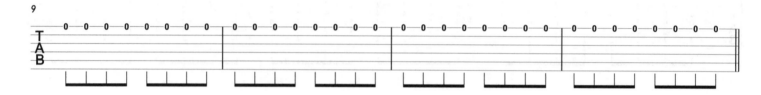

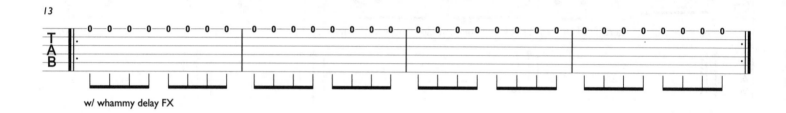

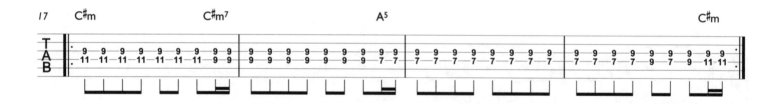

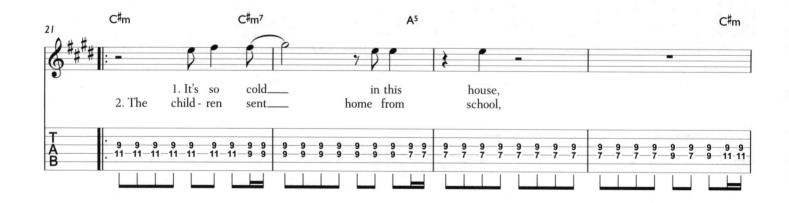

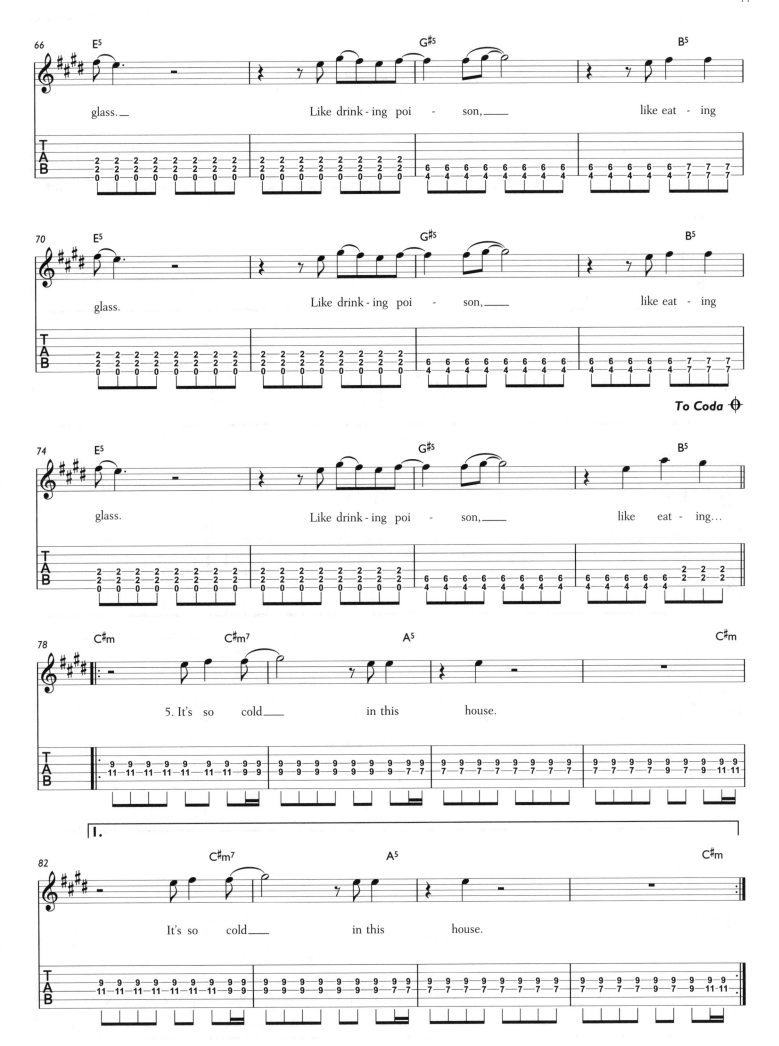

2.

86

C#m7   A5   C#m

It's so cold____ in this_____ bed.__

Coda

90 C#m   C#m7   A5

94 C#m   C#m7   A5

98 C#m   C#m7   A5

We've got   cross-es   on our   eyes,   been walk-ing   in - to   the walls   a - gain.
We've got   cross-es   on our   eyes.   For rich - er,   for poor-er,   for bet - ter, for worse.

1.

102 C#m   C#m7   A5

We've got   cross-es   on our   eyes,   been walk-ing   in - to   the fur - ni - ture.

2.

106 C#m   C#m7   A5

We've got   cross-es   on our   eyes, we've been   walk-ing   in - to   the fur-ni - ture.

Monster

Words and Music by Robin Hawkins, James Frost,
Iwan Griffiths and Alexander Pennie

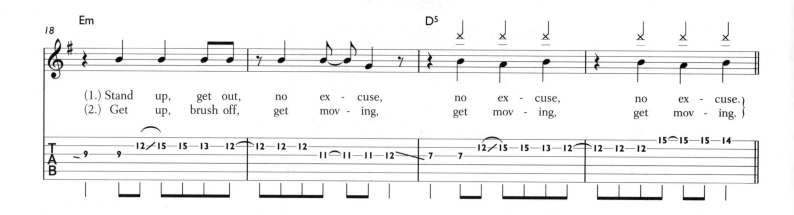

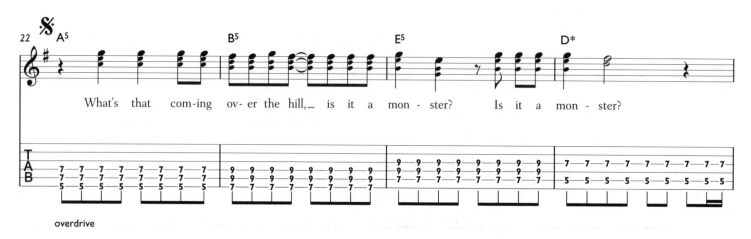

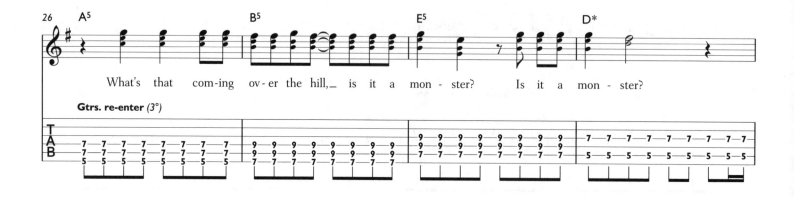

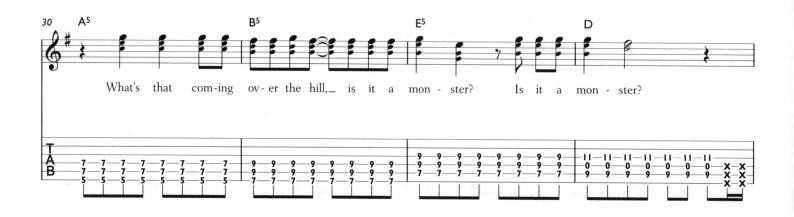

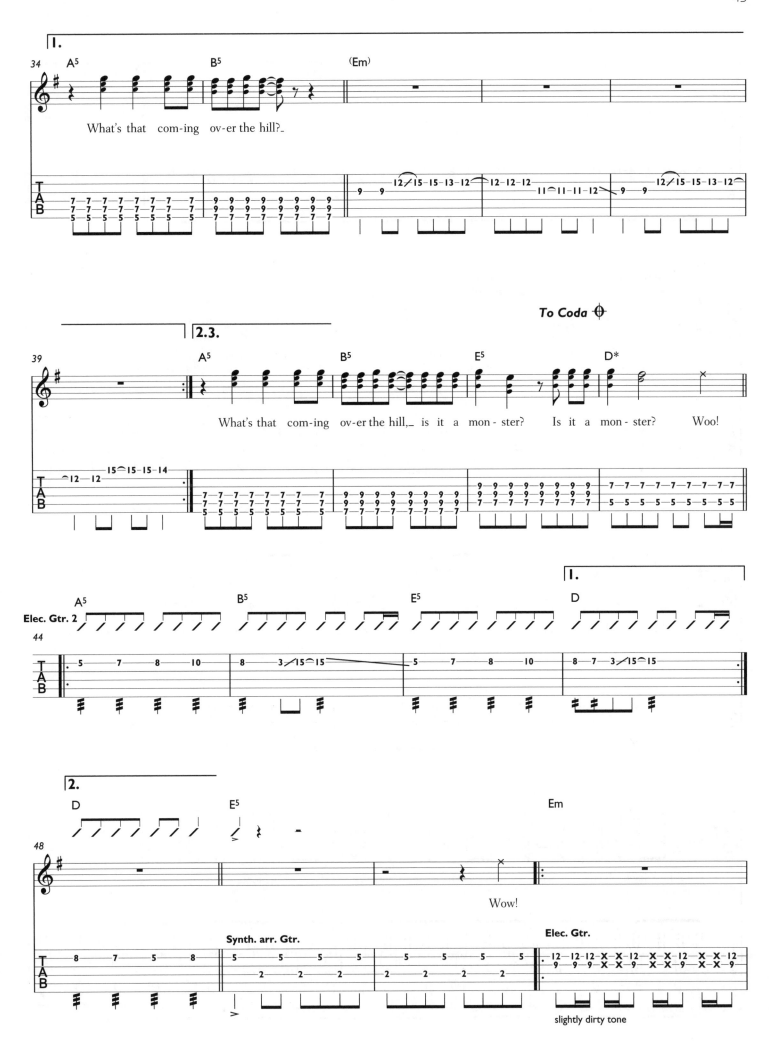

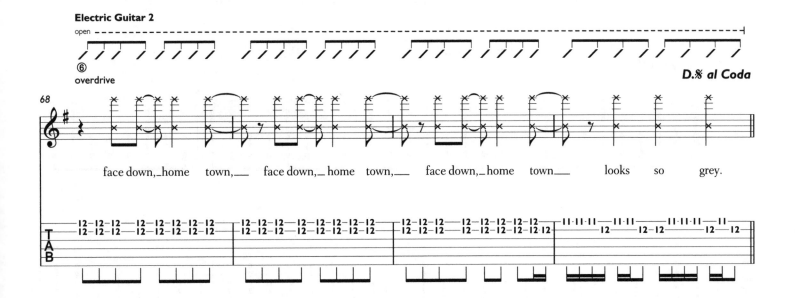

D.% al Coda

face down,_home town,_ face down,_ home town,_ face down,_home town_ looks so grey.

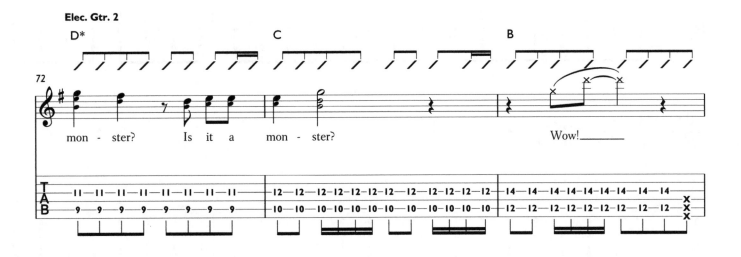

⊕ **Coda**

mon - ster? Is it a mon - ster? Wow!_____

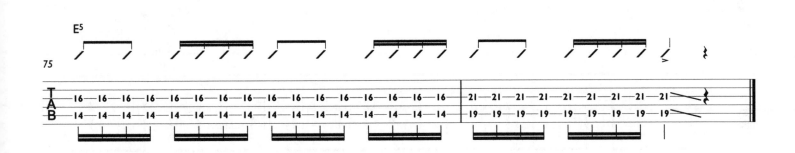

Reason Is Treason

Words and Music by Sergio Pizzorno and Christopher Karloff

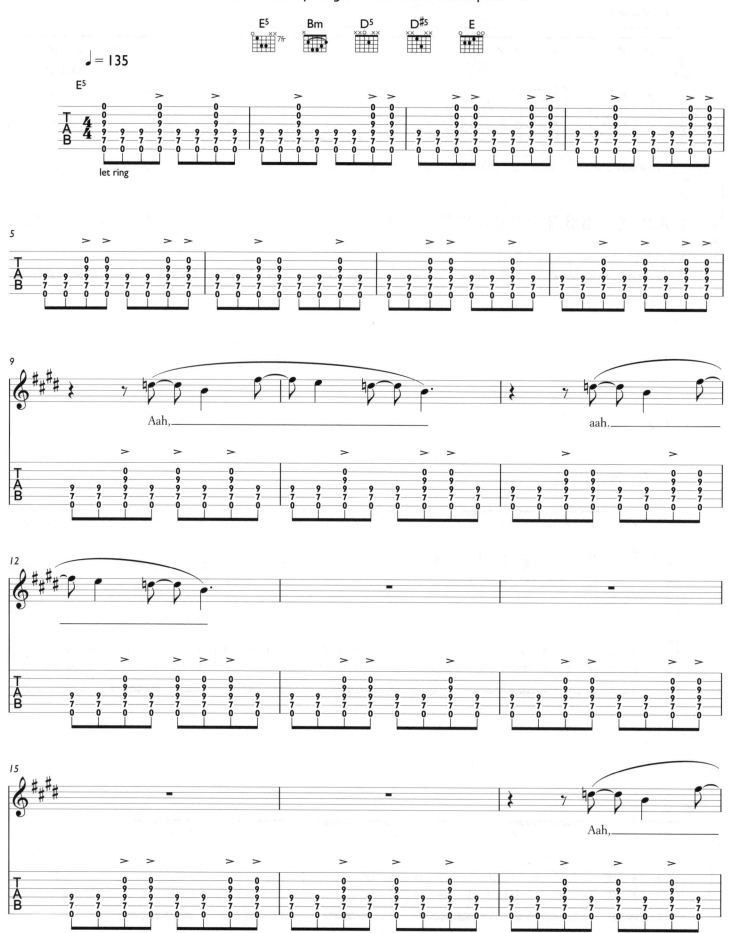

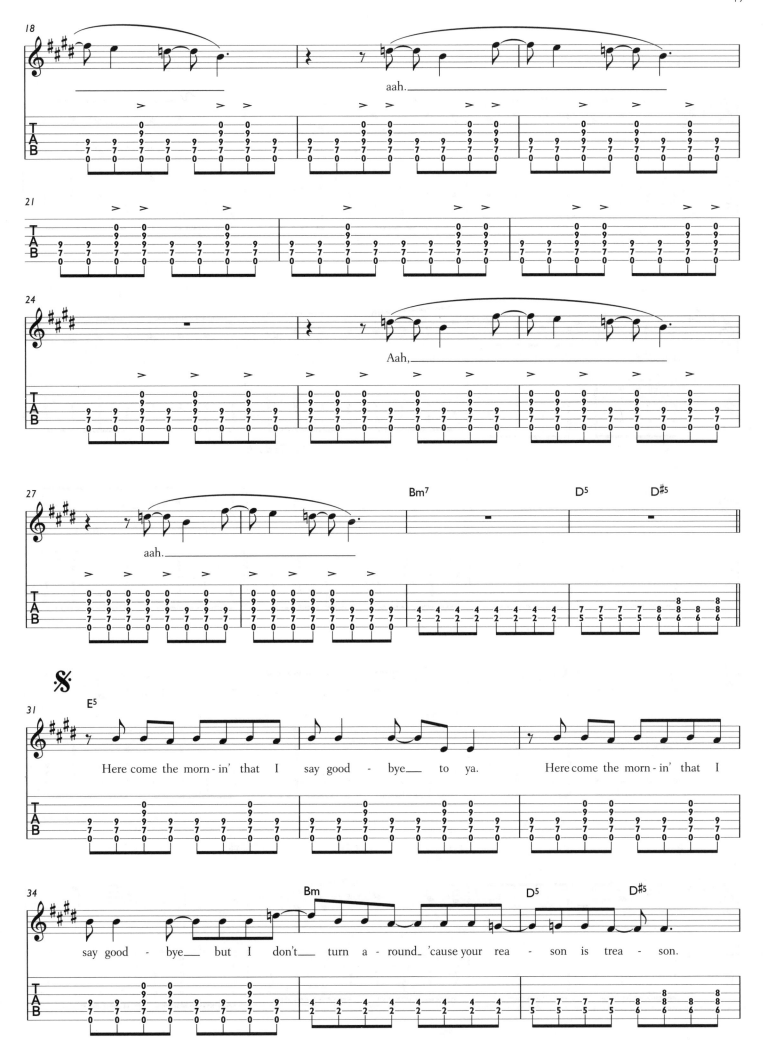

50

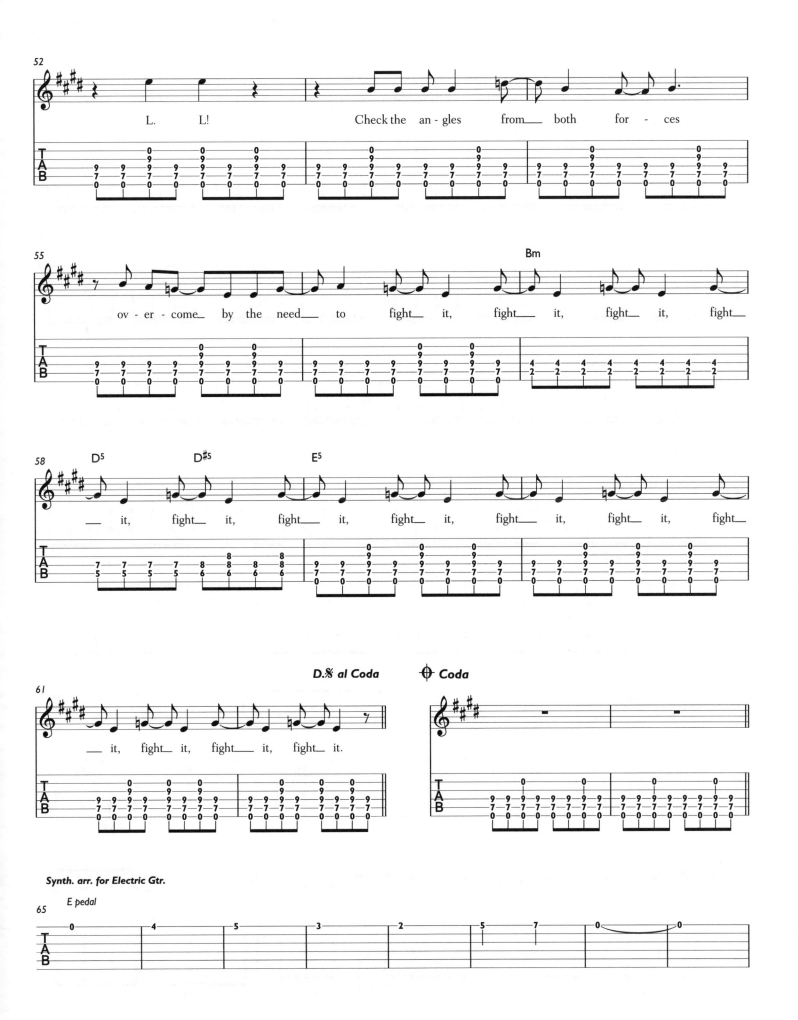

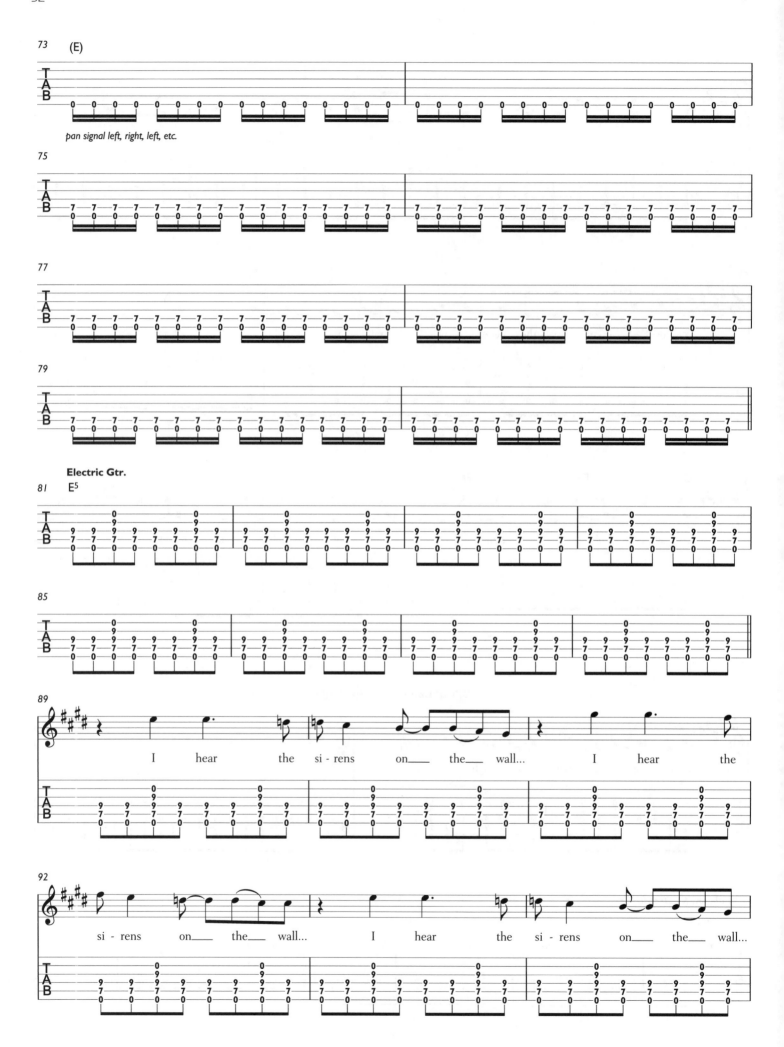

pan signal left, right, left, etc.

Electric Gtr.

I hear the si - rens on___ the___ wall... I hear the

si - rens on___ the___ wall... I hear the si - rens on___ the___ wall...

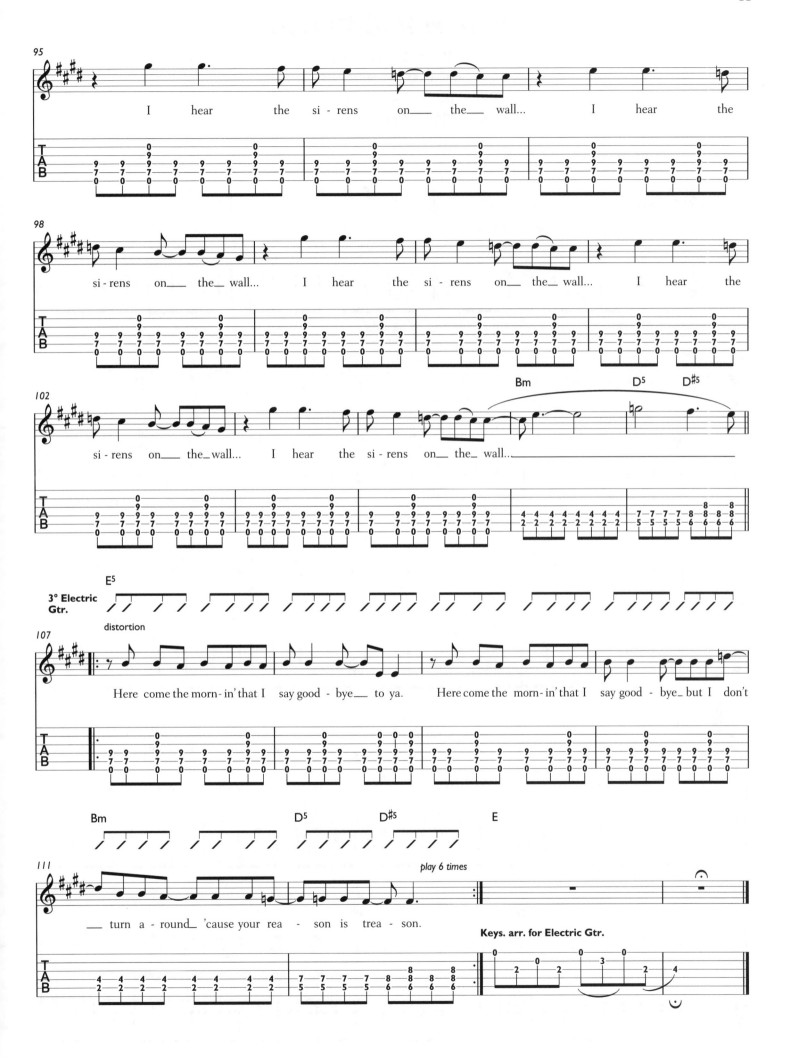

Rock N Roll Queen

Words by Billy Lunn
Music by The Subways

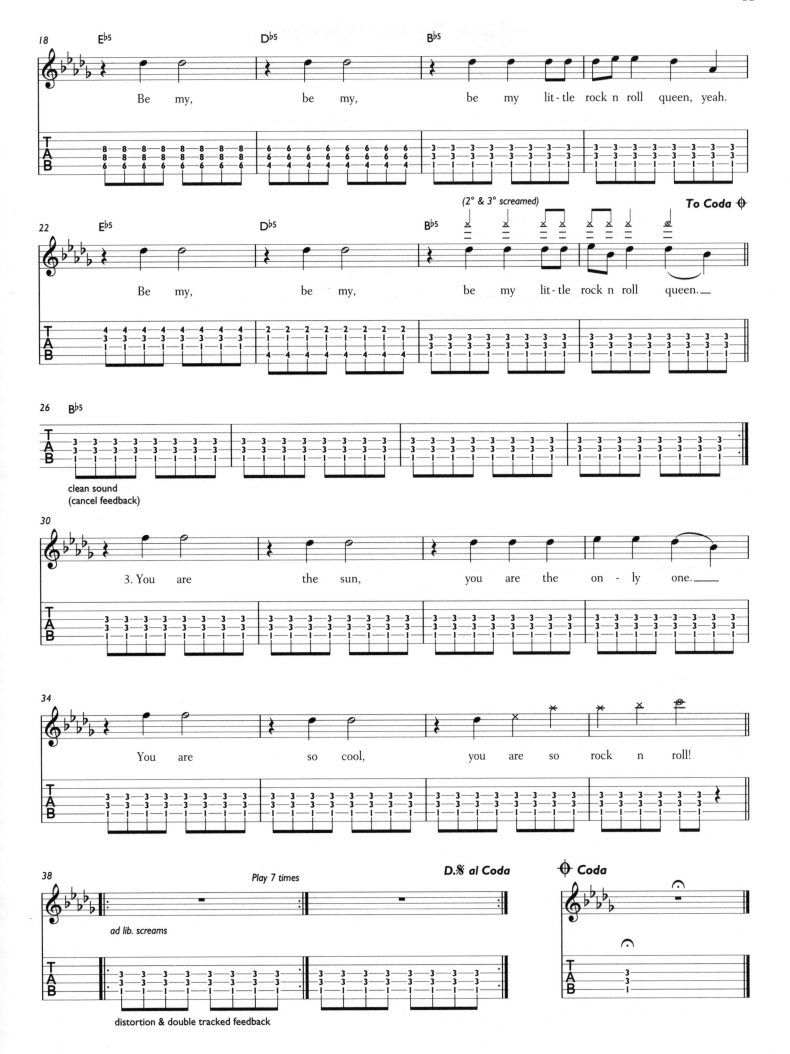

Object Of My Affection

Words and Music by Peter Moren, John Eriksson and Björn Yttling

Snowden

Words and Music by Jimi Goodwin, Jez Williams and Andy Williams

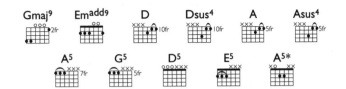

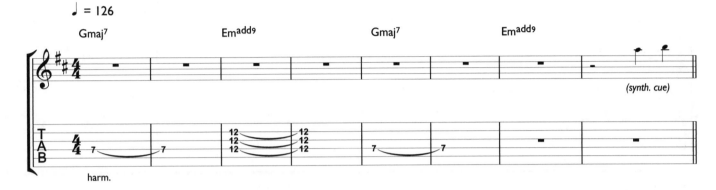

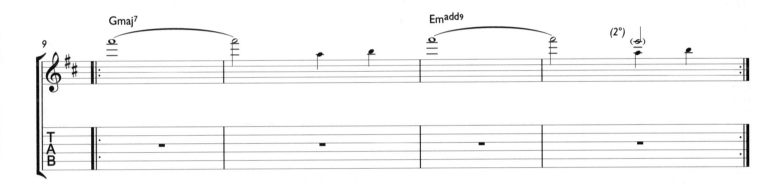

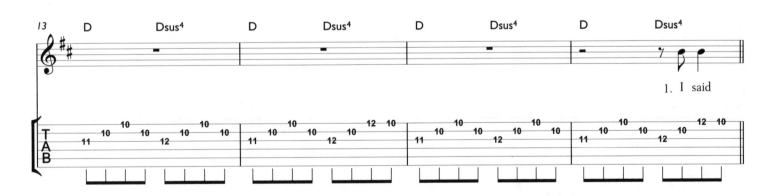

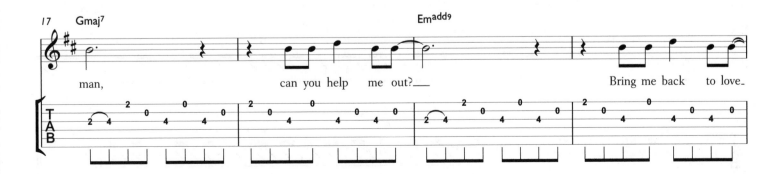

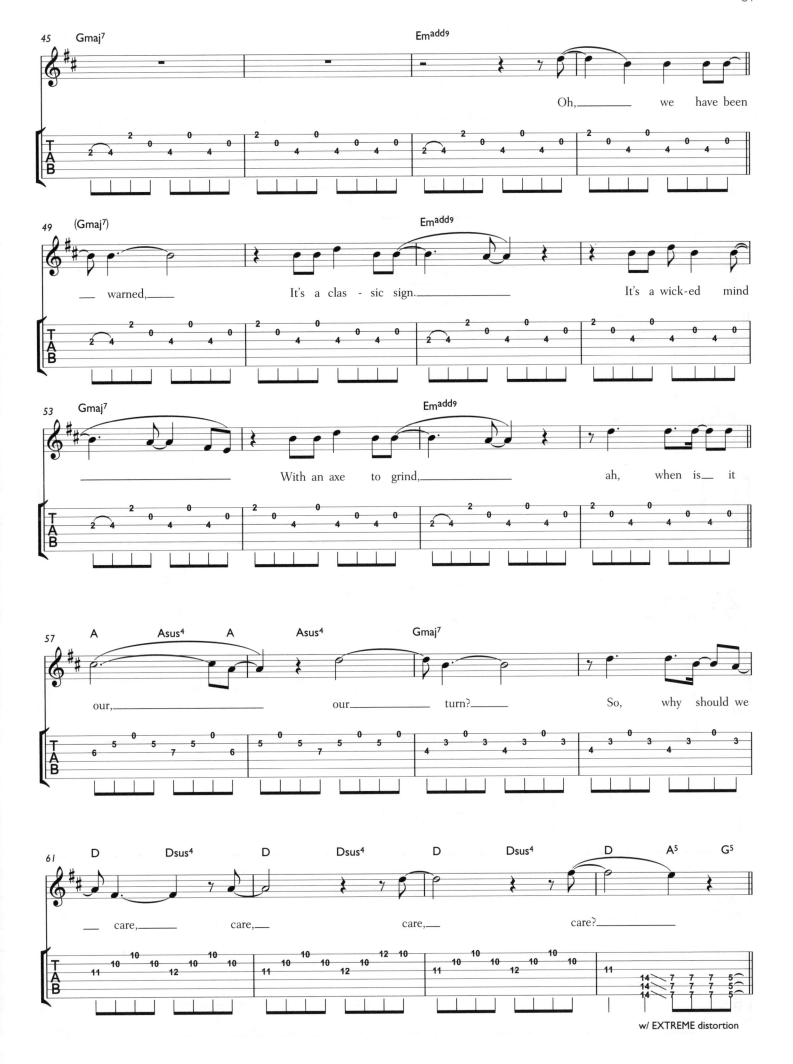

A Town Called Hypocrisy

Words and Music by Ian Watkins, Stuart Richardson,
Richard Oliver, Lee Gaze and Michael Lewis

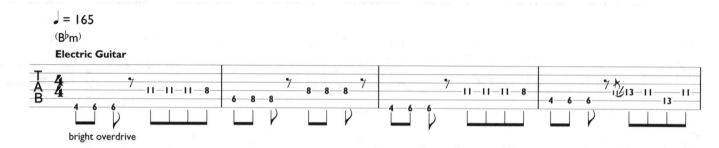

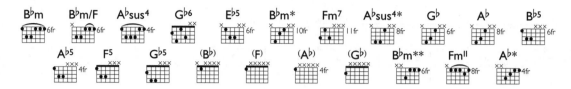

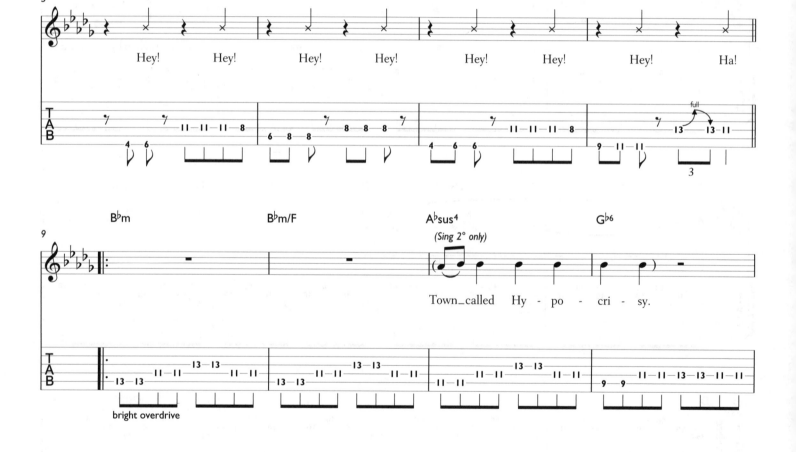

Valerie

Words and Music by Dave McCabe, Sean Payne,
Abigail Harding, Boyan Chowdhury and Russell Pritchard

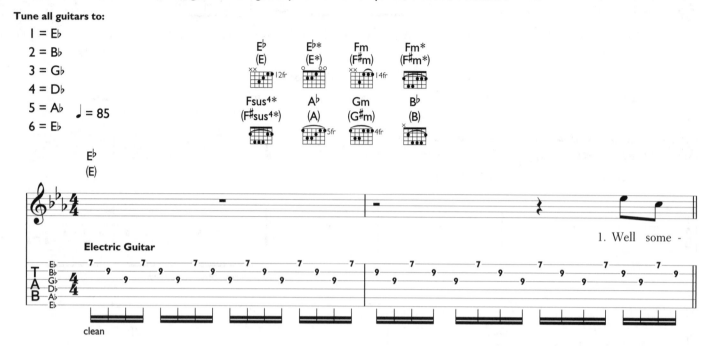

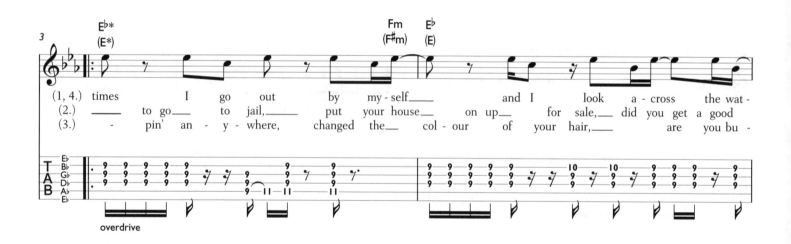

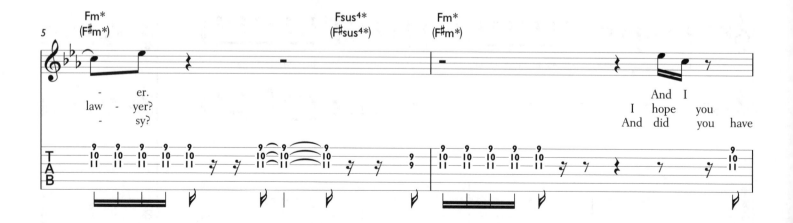

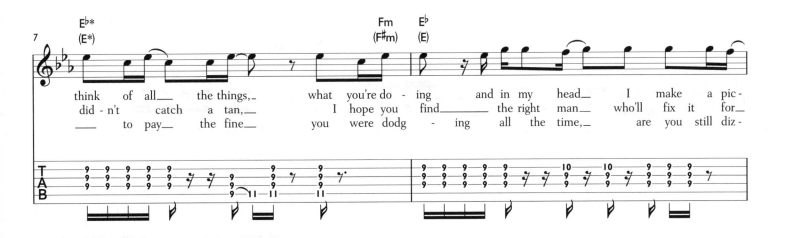

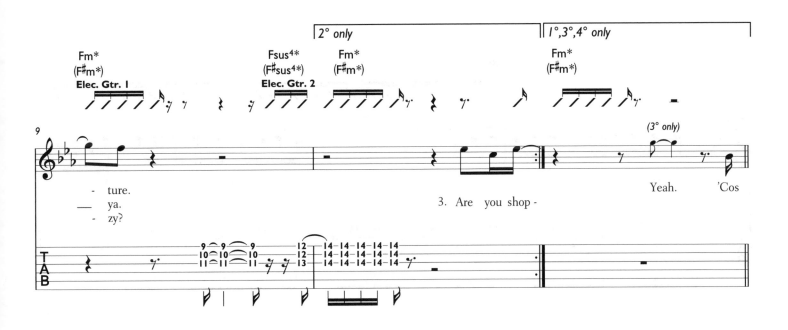

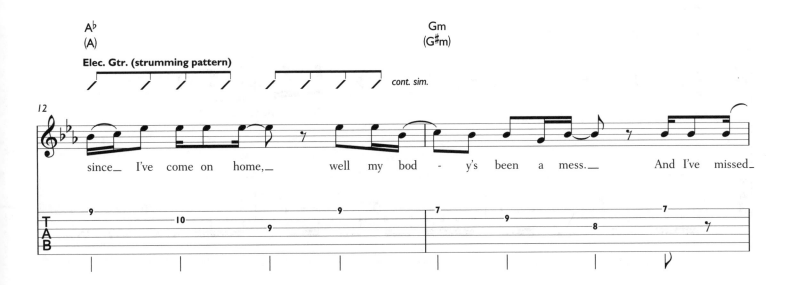

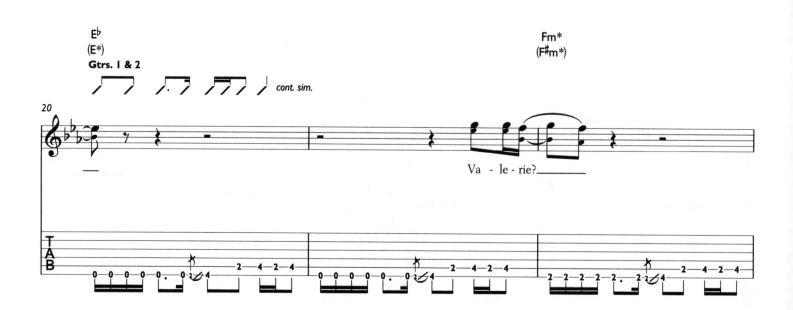

Wake Me Up When September Ends

Words and Music by Billie Joe Armstrong,
Frank E. Wright III and Michael Pritchard

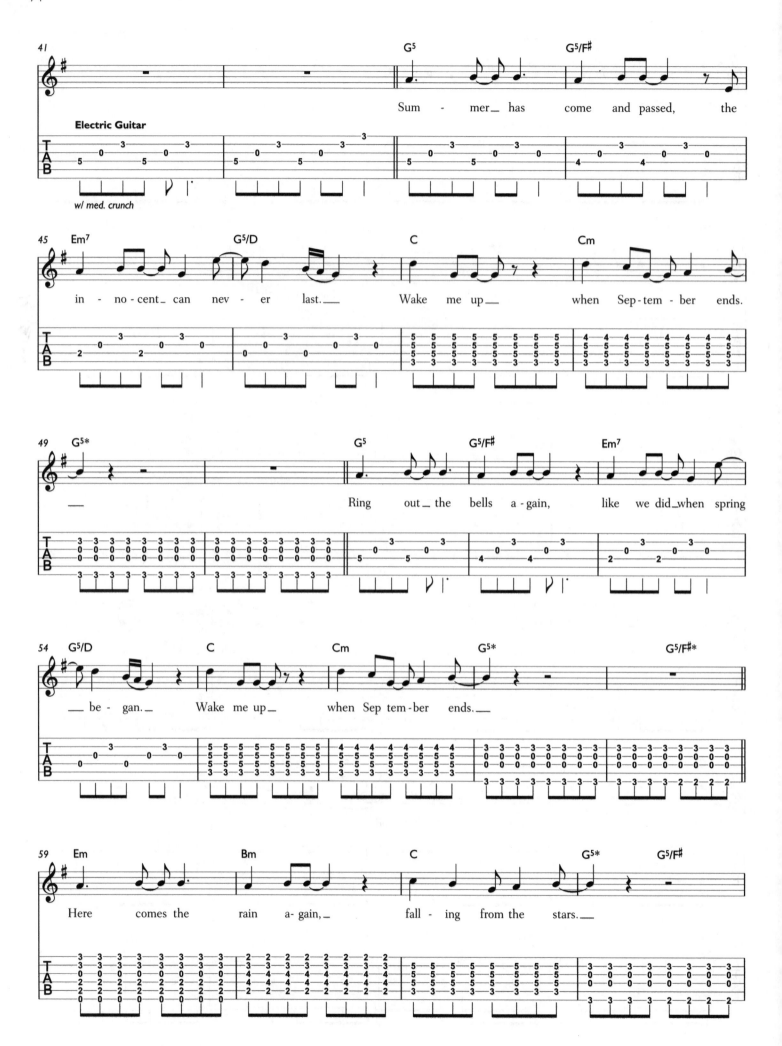

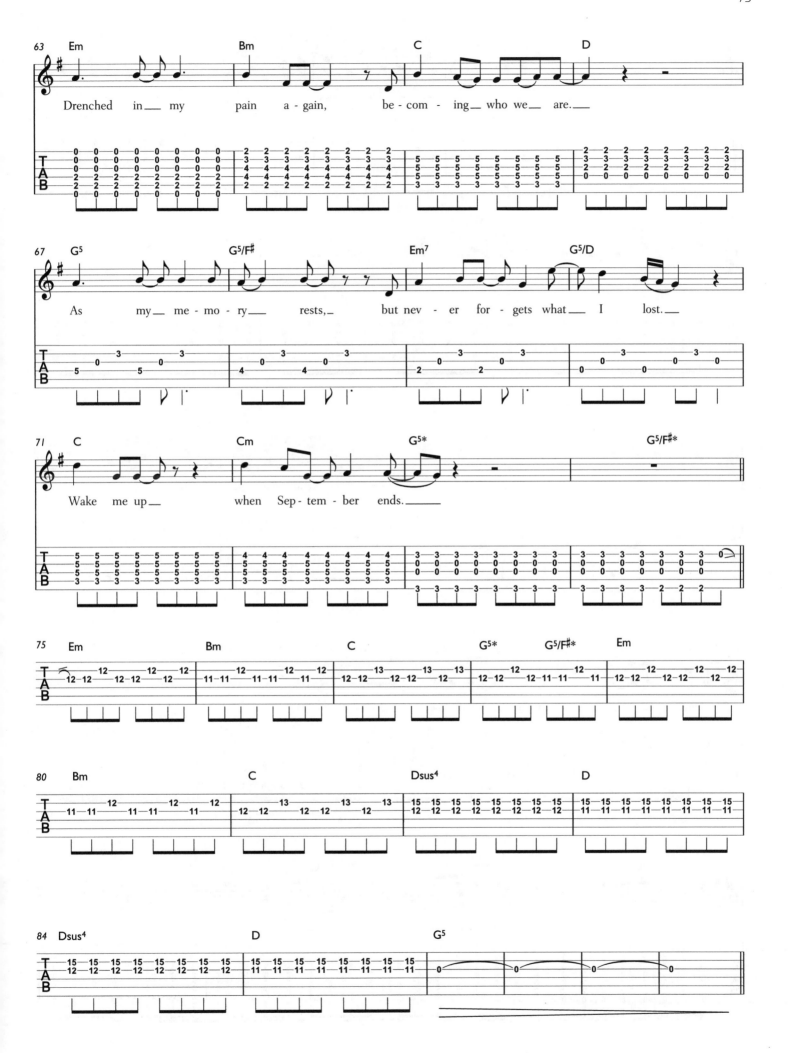

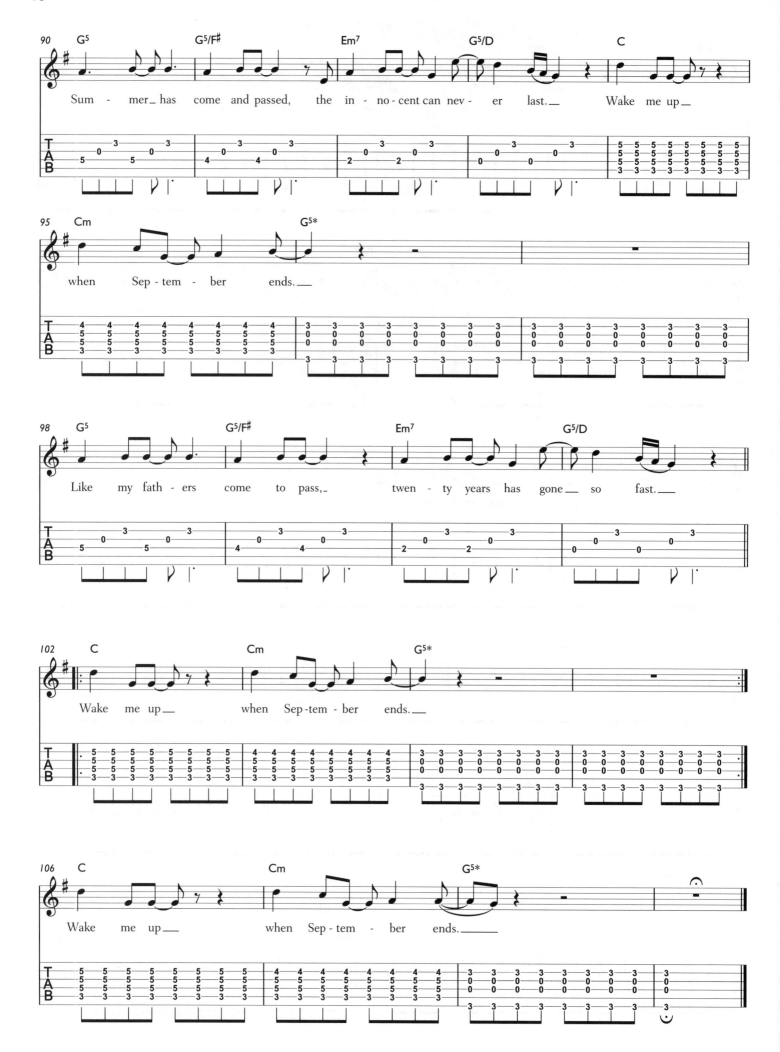

When The Sun Goes Down

Words and Music by Alex Turner

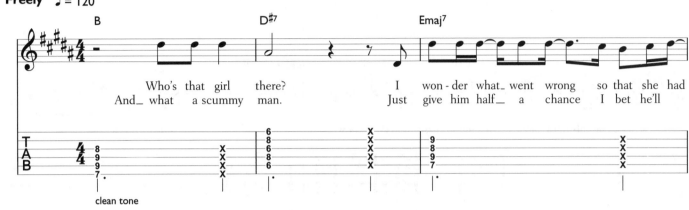

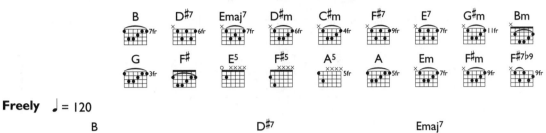

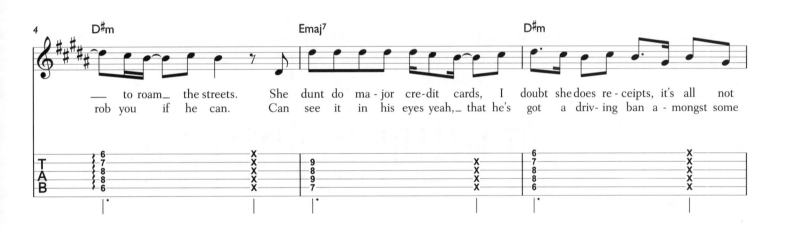

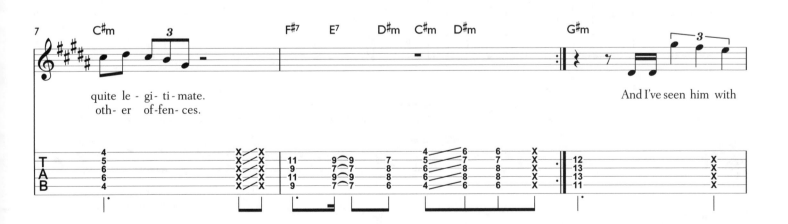

You're All I Have

Words and Music by Gary Lightbody, Nathan Connolly,
Jonathan Quinn, Paul Wilson and Tom Simpson

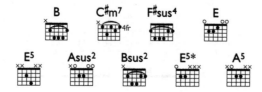

$\quad \bullet = 140$

Synth. Harp arr. for Guitar

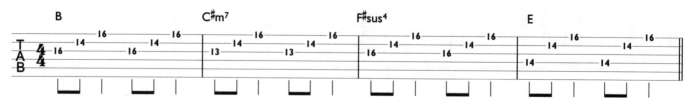

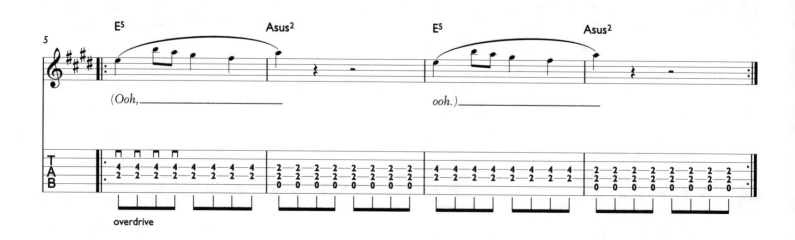

(Ooh,_____ ooh.)_____

overdrive

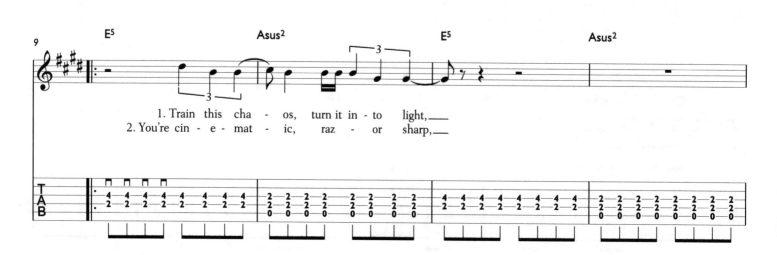

1. Train this cha - os, turn it in - to light,___
2. You're cin - e - mat - ic, raz - or sharp,___

overdrive & octaver

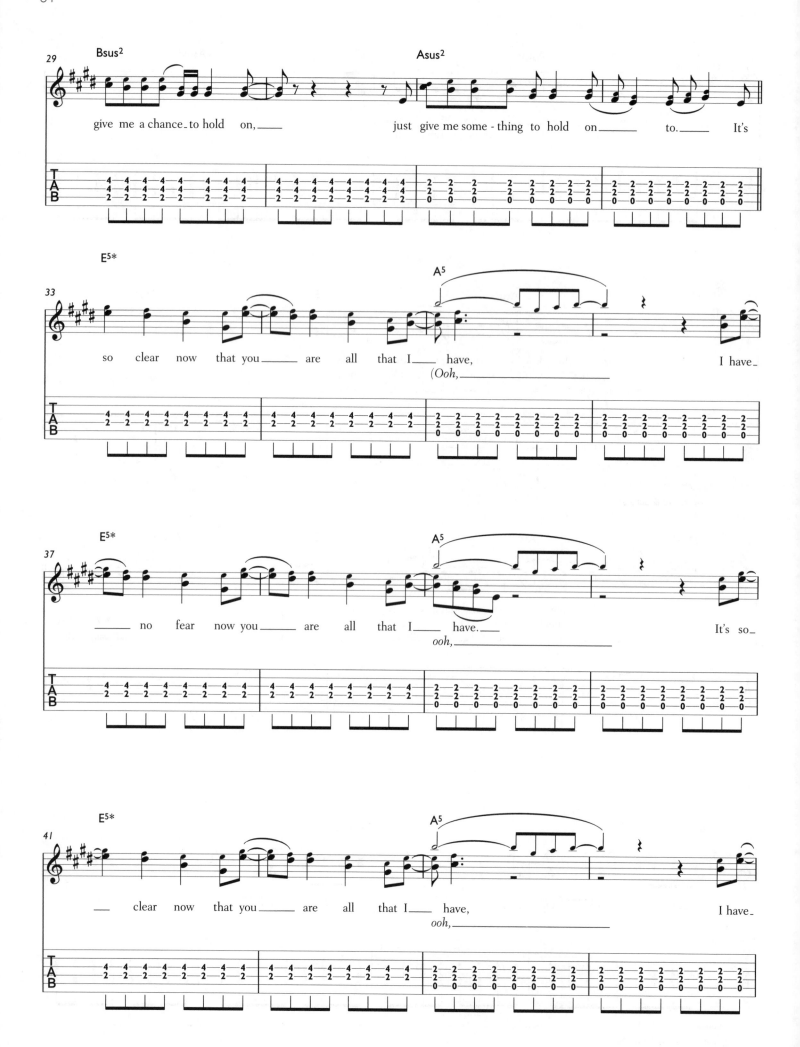

St. Petersburg

Words and Music by Daniel Goffey, Gareth Coombes, Michael Quinn and Robert Coombes

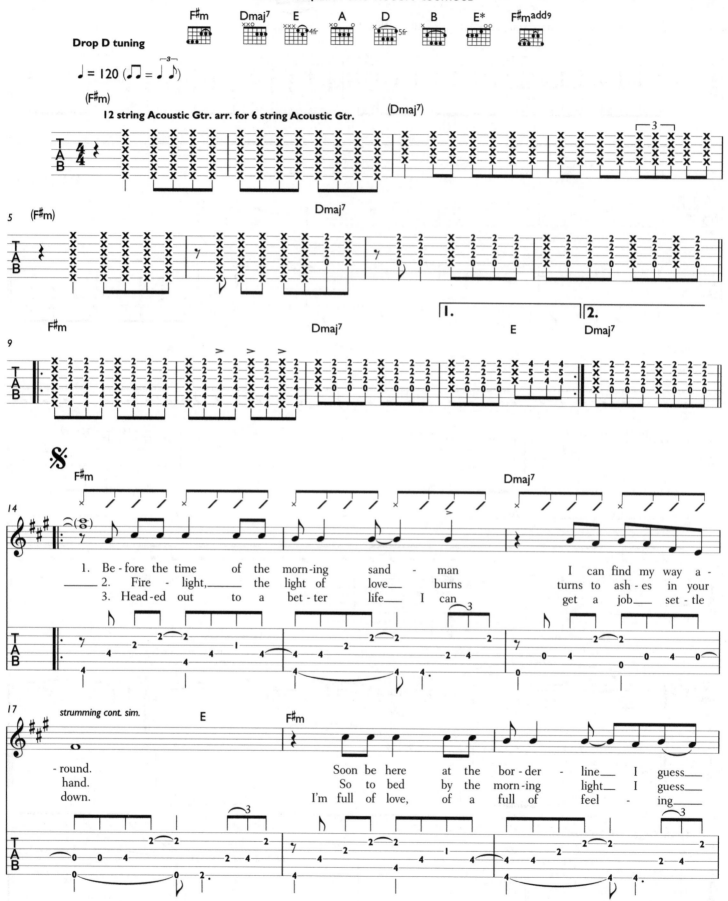

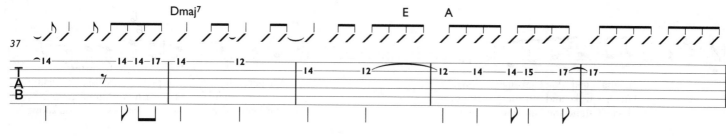

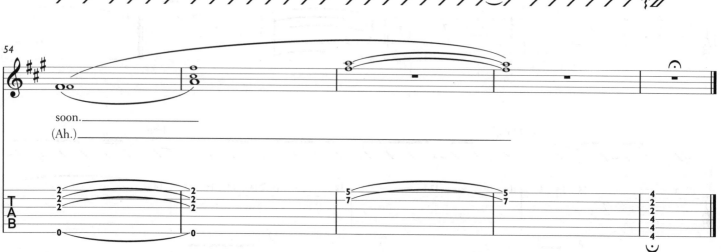